The FIRST BOOK of

mythology

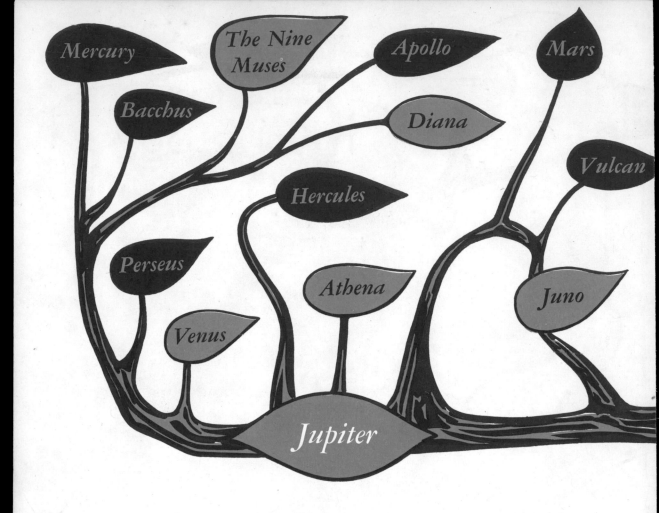

FAMILY TREE

OF THE

Titans and Gods

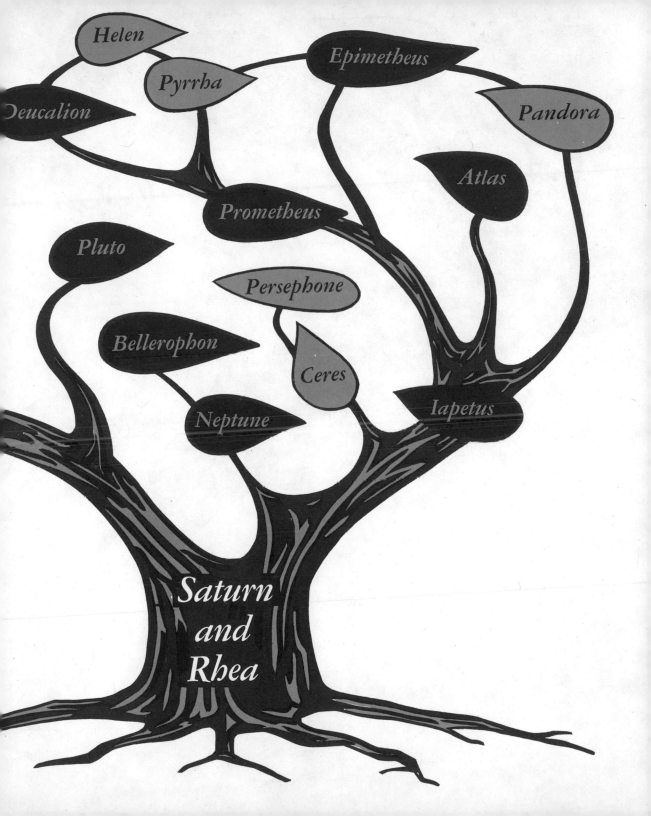

THE FIRST BOOK OF

for Eddie,
may he always believe a
little in these stories.

15 16

Printed in the United States of America by the Polygraphic Company of America

Library of Congress Number: 55-9600

FRANKLIN WATTS, INC.
575 LEXINGTON AVENUE
NEW YORK 22, N. Y.

MYTHOLOGY

GREEK ～ ROMAN

Written and illustrated by KATHLEEN ELGIN

TABLE OF CONTENTS

ne

TALY

Hyperboreans

Mt. Olympus

Mt. Ossa

Mt. Pelion

Mt. Parnassus

ily

Mt. Etna

Delphi

Hellespont

Troy

GREECE

Athens

Lake Stymphalus

Olympia

Sparta

Crete

M E D I T E R R A N E A N   S E A

Africa

THE WORLD
of the Gods

Index of Names and How to Say Them

HOW MYTHS BEGAN

Nobody knows who told the first myth or when he told it. Myths began a long time ago—before scientists found out why the wind blows and the rain falls, why the sun and moon travel across the sky and why the stars come out at night. In those days all the happenings in nature were mysteries. People explained them as best they could by saying that powerful beings called gods ruled everything in nature. The gods ruled the storms and the seasons, the stars and planets and everything that grows on earth. They also ruled such things as love and hate and fun and quarrels.

The Greeks and Romans believed that their gods lived on the high and beautiful mountain which is called Mount Olympus. There were a great many gods, and there were goddesses too. Each one ruled a different thing, so people worshipped those they thought would help them most. There was even a god for thieves to worship!

The Greeks and Romans loved to tell stories about the wonderful adventures of their gods. After a while they added the stories of their heroes, too. To the Greeks and Romans a hero was a warrior who was so much stronger and braver than other people that he seemed almost like a god.

As people told the stories of their gods and heroes over and over, the stories grew and changed. Sometimes people told the same story in several different ways. All these stories make up what we call the Greek and Roman mythology.

1

Even today people find new ways to tell the old myths. You will read them in books and see them in plays and movies and even on television. They are just as interesting today as they were in the beginning, and that is for a strange reason—the Greeks and Romans believed that their gods felt and acted just like human beings! The gods in the myths love and hate, quarrel and make up, play funny tricks and make terrible mistakes, just as we do. The only difference is that everything the gods do is bigger and brighter and noisier.

SOME OF THE GODS AND GODDESSES OF GREECE AND ROME

APOLLO—god of the sun; also god of music and poetry

BACCHUS (also called Dionysus)—god of wine

CERES (also called Demeter)—goddess of plants and harvest

CUPID (also called Eros)—god of love and mischief

ERIS—goddess of quarrels

IRIS—goddess of the rainbow

JUNO (also called Hera)—queen of the gods

JUPITER (also called Zeus)—king of the gods

MERCURY (also called Hermes)—messenger of the gods
    also patron god of thieves

MINERVA (also called Athena)—goddess of wisdom

NEPTUNE (also called Poseidon)—god of the sea

PAN—god of fields and forests and wild animals

PLUTO—god of the underworld

VENUS (also called Aphrodite)—goddess of love and beauty

THE CREATION

Long ago, when the world was young, Heaven and Earth had some children called Titans. The Titans were giants and they ruled the world for many years. The Titans' children were gods and goddesses.

But Saturn, king of the Titans, grew tired of the same company day in, day out. So he asked another Titan, the wise and gentle Prometheus, to make a new creature that was neither bird nor animal nor god.

Prometheus thought a long time, and then he took some clay and modeled a tiny image of himself. Saturn was very pleased. He asked Prometheus to make many more of the tiny images. Then the goddess Minerva breathed life and spirit into them.

And that, the Greeks and Romans believed, is how there came to be men on this earth.

The revolt of the gods

Saturn was such a cruel ruler that the gods and goddesses ran away to make a new kingdom on Mount Olympus. They chose the mighty Jupiter as their king.

When Saturn discovered this he declared war on the gods. He armed the Titans with great rocks, and trees uprooted from the forest. Only Prometheus and two other Titans refused to fight.

When Jupiter looked down from Olympus and saw the terrible army of Titans coming, he threw a blanket of clouds over the mountain to hide it and hurled his lightning through the clouds. The surprised Titans fell back, but they came right on again. The same thing happened over and over for ten long years.

At last Saturn decided that the only way to win the war was to build a mountain higher than Olympus. He told his army to dig the biggest boulders out of Mount Pelion and pile them on Mount Ossa.

But Rhea, mother of the gods, warned Jupiter of Saturn's plan. She also told Jupiter about the Cyclops whom Saturn had imprisoned deep in the earth, and the giants with a hundred arms who were imprisoned with them. The Cyclops knew how to make thunderbolts, and the giants knew how to shake the earth.

Jupiter thanked his mother and hurried down to the underworld. He opened the prison gates and took the Cyclops back to Olympus where they set up a tremendous forge for making thunderbolts. But he told the giants to wait down below.

4

Jupiter allowed the Titans to build their mountain exactly as high as Mount Olympus. Then he gave the signal for attack. The gods hurled their new thunderbolts and the Titans' mountain burst into flames. The grass burned and the trees burned and the smoke of their burning hid the sun. Then the giants in the underworld began to shake the earth with their hundred arms. The Titans' mountain quaked and trembled until it broke apart and the Titans fell down, down into the ruins. Jupiter was king of the whole world.

The great gift of fire

When Jupiter first ruled the world there was everlasting spring on earth. But Jupiter grew tried of the same weather day after day. He wanted something very cold and something very hot, and he wanted the mild seasons in between. So he created summer, and then he created fall and the cold, cold winter.

Down on earth Prometheus walked among the men he had made so long ago and saw them huddled together for warmth, stumbling in the long dark of the winter night. He knew that they would die without warmth and light, so he asked Jupiter to give them fire. But Jupiter knew that if men had fire they would be almost as powerful as gods, and so he refused.

Then Prometheus decided to risk Jupiter's anger and steal the fire of heaven. He hid himself on the road where the god Apollo drove the golden chariot of the sun across the sky. When the chariot flew by he held a dried reed against one of the fiery wheels. The reed sparked and blazed a little and Prometheus hid the flame between his hands and carried it back to earth so that men could have light and warmth.

When Jupiter found out what Prometheus had done he was terribly angry. He commanded two giants, Force and Vulcan, to carry Prometheus to a high and lonely mountain peak and bind him there with chains. There Prometheus lay for hundreds of years until the great hero Hercules came to free him.

Pandora's box

But Jupiter's anger was still so strong that he decided he must also punish the men Prometheus had given the fire to. He thought of the oddest way to do it. He made a woman. Her name was Pandora. All the gods gave her gifts. Jupiter gave her a little box which he warned her never to open, and then he sent her down to earth.

One of Pandora's gifts was curiosity. She wanted to touch, taste, smell and look into everything in sight. Of course she was curious to know what was in the little box, and finally she decided to take just one tiny peek under the lid.

But when Pandora lifted its lid the most terrible things flew out of the box—sickness and sorrow and despair. She tried to shut them back in the box but it was too late. They flew all over the earth. There was just one thing left in the box, and that was hope. Ever since then men have kept hope in their hearts to help them fight the bad things that escaped from Pandora's box.

The flood

Jupiter ruled the world for many hundreds of years. Then one day he began to wonder how the people on earth were getting along. Disguising himself as a human being, he went down to see for himself.

Everywhere Jupiter went he found trouble. People were greedy and jealous and quarrelsome. They no longer had any reverence for the gods.

Jupiter was so angry that he went back to Olympus determined to remove every single man and woman from the beautiful earth they had spoiled. He covered the whole sky with clouds and commanded the winds to whip and twist them. Into the whirling mass he sent the rain, and the rain poured down into the rivers and the sea and over all the earth. The flood rose higher and higher.

The frightened people fled up the highest mountains, but the

10

flood rose over the mountains. When at last the rain stopped, there were only two people left on earth. They were Deucalion and his wife Pyrrha, who had climbed to the top of Mount Parnassus. Jupiter spared them because they were good.

When the sun dried the earth again, Deucalion and Pyrrha found a temple, half ruined and covered with wet moss. Here they thanked the gods for saving them and prayed that someone on Olympus would tell them what to do all alone on earth. A voice answered them from the temple. It told them to go down from the mountain and as they went, to throw stones ahead of them. Deucalion and Pyrrha did this, and as the stones fell, they changed slowly into men and women.

In this way, in the time the Greeks and Romans called the Stone Age, human beings came to live on earth again. The wonderful stories in mythology are about these people and their children and their grandchildren and the gods they lived with.

11

THE FIRST FLIGHT

Daedalus was an architect, a builder of temples and houses. On the island of Crete he built a labyrinth, a strange house with secret, twisting passageways and walks. It was for the Minotaur, the favorite monster of King Minos.

But as kings sometimes will, King Minos lost his temper over some small thing and locked Daedalus and his son Icarus in a tower. They escaped from the tower, but they could not escape from the island. King Minos watched all the ships.

"Very well," said Daedalus, "if we can't escape by sea, we'll try the sky. We shall fly, Icarus."

So Daedalus and Icarus set to work making wings from the feathers of many birds. They held the feathers together with wax and thread. At last they finished two pairs of wings and Daedalus fitted one pair to his own shoulders. Moving them slowly, like a great bird, he soared into the air. How beautiful it was! Icarus could hardly wait to try his own wings.

Daedalus returned soon and came down softly onto the grass. He helped Icarus fasten on his wings, and Icarus learned very quickly how to use them. After several days of practice, Daedalus and Icarus were ready to escape from the cruel king.

"Remember, Icarus," said Daedalus, "stay with me and you will be safe. Don't fly too high or the sun will melt your wings. And be careful not to fly too low, or the sea's mists will clog your wings."

12

Icarus promised to be careful, but once he was in the air and felt his strong wings bearing him upward, he forgot his promise. Higher and higher he flew until he was so far above the earth that he could not hear his father's warning shouts. The air grew thin. The burning sun rushed toward him and one small feather fluttered from his wings.

It was too late when Icarus felt the burn of the melting wax on his shoulders. His beautiful wings shed their feathers like leaves. Down, down he fell, so swiftly that his father could not reach him before he plunged into the sea.

Daedalus searched the water for his son for many days, but he never found him. At last he flew on alone and came to Sicily. There he built a temple to Apollo and hung up his wings as an offering to the god.

THE RACE FOR ATALANTA

Atalanta was so swift of foot that the fastest runners in Greece could not outdistance her. She was also so beautiful that all the young men wanted to marry her. But a fortune teller had warned her that if she married she would be unhappy, so she stayed away from young men. She said she would marry only the one who could outrun her, and she would put to death any who tried and failed.

Young Hippomenes could not understand why so many young men were glad to die for Atalanta. Then he saw her and fell in love with her himself. Like the others, he challenged her to a race, but first he asked Venus to help him. Venus gave him three golden apples and told him how to use them.

When Atalanta saw Hippomenes she was not sure that she wanted to conquer him. He was so young and handsome that it

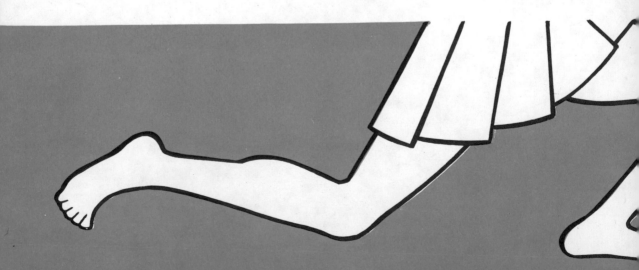

seemed a pity that he should die for her sake. She almost wished he would give up the race.

During the first part of the race Atalanta managed to keep just a little ahead of Hippomenes. He was very swift. But his breath came harder and harder and Atalanta knew that he was tired. Then suddenly he tossed one of the golden apples in her path. She looked at it in surprise and stopped to pick it up. Hippomenes dashed ahead. Then Atalanta gathered all her strength and caught up with him and passed him. But Hippomenes threw another apple and again Atalanta stopped to pick it up. He passed her, but she sped ahead again.

In desperation Hippomenes tossed the last apple onto the side of the course. Now Atalanta knew she would lose the race if she turned aside to pick up the apple. But she really wanted Hippomenes to win. She swerved off-course, picked up the apple, and Hippomenes dashed past her to the goal.

15

THE GOLDEN TOUCH

Bacchus, the god of wine, offered to grant King Midas his dearest wish. The foolish king wished that everything he touched would turn to gold. Bacchus granted him his wish.

That evening King Midas, strolling in his garden, touched the smallest branch on his apple tree. The branch turned immediately to purest gold. He picked an apple and the apple turned to gold. Delighted with his new power, Midas ordered a great feast of celebration. He invited all his friends, for he wanted them to see what he could do.

When all his guests had arrived, Midas took his place at the head of the table and raised his glass in a toast to Bacchus. The guests raised their glasses, too, then stared in amazement at the king. Midas had dashed his glass angrily to the floor, and from it there poured not wine, but liquid gold!

Frantically Midas broke a piece of bread. It turned to gold too. He threw it on the table and picked up a bunch of grapes. Heavy and cold and golden the grapes slipped through his trembling fingers. Golden wine and golden bread and golden fruit! thought Midas. I shall slowly starve to death.

King Midas tried every way he could think of to rid himself of the golden touch. At last he went to Bacchus and asked him to take away his foolish gift. Bacchus told him to go to the magic river Factolus and bathe in its waters. Midas did, and washed his golden touch away.

From that day on Midas hated gold. He lived as simply as ordinary people do. Roaming the woods and hills and loving them, he finally became a follower of Pan, god of the fields.

Pan was a strange god—half goat, half man. He played strange and beautiful music on some little pipes he had made from the river reeds. One day he challenged the great Apollo to a musical contest. Apollo brought his silver lyre. They chose the mountain Tmolus to be the judge.

Pan played first. As the thin sweet music of his pipes rose on the air the trees all clapped their leaves together in delight. Then Apollo played. The music of his silver lyre rose higher than Olympus. The mountain Tmolus cried out that surely Apollo had won.

But Midas, who thought the music of the fields the sweetest in the world, argued that Pan had won. This made Apollo so angry that he said Midas had ears like an ass. The instant Apollo spoke, Midas felt his ears begin to grow. They grew and grew until they were just the size of an ass's ears, and they had fur on them, inside and out.

Midas was so ashamed that he wound a turban around his head and never took it off. Nobody knew his secret but his hairdresser, and he said he would not tell. But the secret was too good to keep. The hairdresser whispered it into a hole in the ground. Some reeds grew over the hole and they whispered the secret to the wind. If you listen to the wind in the reeds today you will hear it whisper, "Midas has ass's ears!"

18

THE TWELVE LABORS OF HERCULES

One of the greatest heroes of ancient Greece was Hercules. He was not afraid of anything. But he had a quick temper, and when he was angry he challenged even the gods. Juno disliked Hercules and made trouble for him all his life. When he was a young man she sent him to serve the harsh King Eurystheus in Nemea in southern Greece. Eurystheus sent Hercules on the adventures we call the "Twelve Labors of Hercules."

Hercules' first labor was the quest of a terrible lion which roamed the land and frightened everybody. The lion was so strong and fierce that even the greatest hunters could not capture it.

Hercules found the lion after a long hunt. He shot his great arrows at the beast, but its skin was so tough that the arrows just

bounced off it. Then Hercules hit the lion with his club, but he could not hurt it that way either. It was the strongest lion he had ever seen. Finally he just wound his arms around the beast's neck and choked the life out of it.

Then Eurystheus sent Hercules to kill the Hydra, a snake-like beast which lived in a swamp just outside the town. The Hydra had nine heads on nine long necks and the middle head was immortal. Hercules attacked it boldly with his sword, for he did not know that the thing had a special trick. Every time that he struck off one of the fearful heads, the Hydra grew two new ones in its place! Finally Hercules had to call his servant, Iolus. Iolus brought a torch and they burned off all the mortal heads before the Hydra could grow any new ones. They rolled a boulder over the immortal head and that was the end of the Hydra. It has never frightened anybody since.

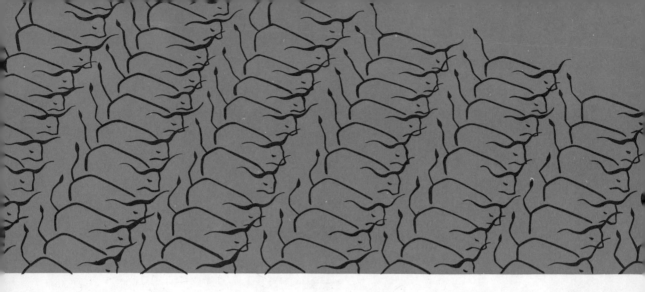

Hercules' third labor was to clean the stable of King Augeas of Elis on the Ionian Sea. Augeas had three thousand oxen and he had not cleaned their stables in thirty years. It was a task for a giant, but Hercules had a giant's strength. He made the rivers Alpheus and Peneus run through the stables and cleaned them in one day.

The fourth labor of Hercules was to bring to Eurystheus' daughter the golden battle girdle of the queen of the Amazons, Hippolyta. The Amazons were fierce women warriors who lived across the sea. Hercules was prepared for a battle. But Hippolyta admired Hercules so much that she gave him the girdle willingly.

Juno was angry because Hercules had won so easily. She wanted to make trouble for him. So she told the Amazons that he had tricked Hippolyta. The Amazons charged the ship just as Hercules was about to sail. Of course Hercules thought that Hippolyta had tricked him. In revenge, he killed her.

The fifth labor of Hercules was to bring to the king the beautiful oxen of Geryon, a monster with three bodies and three heads and many arms and legs and wings. Geryon kept a giant and a fierce two-headed dog to guard his oxen.

When Hercules set sail for Erytheia, where Geryon lived, he found a mountain in his way. He could not sail through it and he did not want to sail around it, so he broke it into two mountains and sailed between them. The mountains are called the Pillars of Hercules. They guard the Straits of Gibraltar.

At last Hercules reached Erytheia. Secretly he stole to the field where the oxen grazed. The dog was sleeping by the giant's side, but as soon as Hercules came near, the dog awoke and attacked him with snapping jaws. Hercules fought off the dog first and killed it. Then he wound his arms around the giant and wrestled with him until the giant too lay dead. Then Hercules herded the oxen onto his ship and sailed for home.

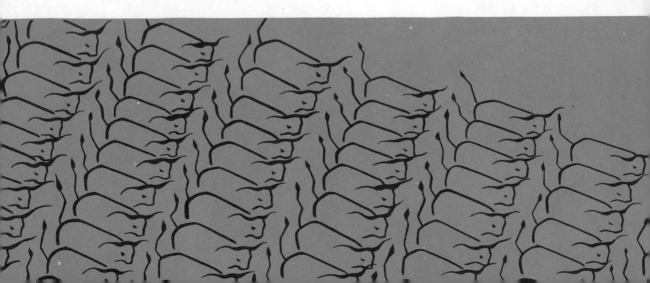

The sixth labor of Hercules took a whole year. The king sent him to bring back the Cerynean stag, a wild deer which belonged to the goddess Minerva. This was not a labor that needed strength and courage. It needed patience, for the stag was wild and shy and hid itself in the leafy woods. Hercules was not used to being patient. He wasn't used to being quiet either, and he had to be very quiet as he stalked the timid deer. When at last he caught it and led it to the king, he was more tired than he was from any of his other labors.

Then the king sent Hercules to capture a wild boar. Through dark forests and deep valleys and over towering mountains Hercules trailed the fierce beast. When winter came and snow covered the ground, the chase was easier. He could follow the boar's tracks. At last he tracked it to its cave in the rocks. By then the animal was too cold and tired to fight. Hercules captured it easily.

The eighth labor of Hercules was a battle against the terrible

Stymphalian birds which were frightening the people of Stymphalus. There were thousands of these birds. They had claws as strong as steel, and their quills were sharp as arrows. They could shoot their quills like arrows, too.

Hercules fought these birds in a strange way. He clanged a bell and drummed loudly on his shield. The birds flew to see what the noise was. When they saw Hercules they shot their quills at him. But the quills struck his shield and fell harmlessly to the ground. When the birds had shot all their quills, most of them flew away in fright. Hercules shot the rest of them with his great bow and arrows.

Now the king sent Hercules to tame a savage white bull which the god Neptune had given to King Minos of Crete. Hercules grabbed the bull by its long white horns and with his great strength wrestled it to the ground. The bull lost all its fierceness after that, and Hercules led it quietly to King Minos.

25

Hercules' tenth labor was to tame a pair of horses which belonged to King Diomedes. The horses were so strong and wild that nobody could put a bridle on them. They charged Hercules, breathing fire and cutting the air with their iron hoofs. But Hercules just wound his powerful arms around their necks and threw them to the ground. The horses knew they had met their master. They followed Hercules peacefully to their stable.

For his next labor, Eurystheus sent Hercules to get the golden apples of the Hesperides. The Hesperides were the three fair daughters of the Titan, Atlas. On the road Hercules had to travel there was a giant named Antaeus. Antaeus challenged everyone who passed to a wrestling match and he always won.

Hercules wrestled with Antaeus for hours, but he could not conquer the giant. Every time Hercules threw him to the ground, Antaeus leaped up with new strength. Then suddenly Hercules guessed the giant's secret. Antaeus got his strength from his mother,

Earth. As long as Antaeus touched the ground, his mother poured strength into him. Hercules lifted Antaeus off the ground and held him there until all his strength drained away.

At last Hercules came to Mount Atlas in Africa where Atlas stood holding up the sky on his shoulders. Hercules asked Atlas if he would get the apples for him, but Atlas said he had to stay there and hold up the sky or it would fall down. Hercules said he would be glad to hold the sky if Atlas would get the apples.

Atlas eased the sky onto Hercules' shoulders and said he would be back soon. But when he returned with the golden apples he was in no hurry to shoulder the sky again. He said he would be very happy to take the apples to the king himself.

Hercules knew better than to be tricked into holding up the sky forever! He thanked Atlas for his offer, but at the same time he took the golden apples, shifted the sky back onto the Titan's shoulders and hurried away to the king.

27

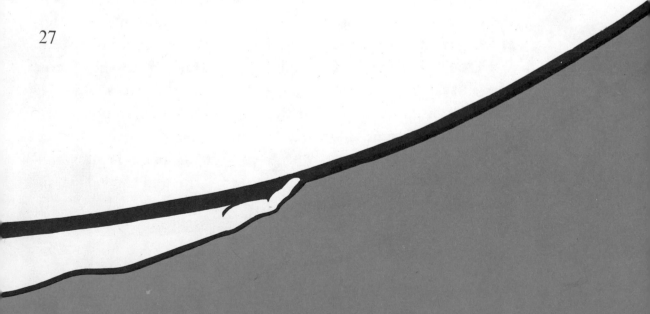

The last labor of Hercules took him to the dark underworld of Pluto, where Pluto kept a dog named Cerberus. The dog had three heads and a dragon's tail. King Eurystheus had never seen a monster like that, so he asked Hercules to bring the dog up to the Earth so he could see it.

Pluto told Hercules he might borrow the dog if he could capture it without using any weapons. Hercules promised not to harm Cerberus and he promised to return him soon.

When Hercules entered the cave where Cerberus lived he saw six yellow eyes glaring at him out of the darkness. Then with three terrible growls from his three terrible throats the dog leaped at Hercules. Bracing himself on the slimy floor of the cave Hercules grabbed the dog around the middle before it could reach him. Then he held it high above his head so that the three angry jaws could not snap at him.

Hercules carried the three-headed dog out of the underworld this way, up to the earth and the sweet warm air. Then, when Eurystheus had looked at the ugly beast as long as he wanted to, Hercules carried it in the same way back to the underworld.

Hercules had many more adventures. He lived a long, heroic life. But he did not die heroically in battle, as a hero should. He died of a poison his wife had washed his clothes in, a poison she thought was a magic charm which would make him love her more.

After he died, Hercules was given a great honor. Jupiter himself came down to earth in a four-horse chariot and carried Hercules back to heaven to live among the stars.

28

ECHO AND NARCISSUS

The beautiful nymph Echo liked to talk and argue. She never tired of it, and so she usually had the last word in any argument. She even argued with the goddess Juno and won. This made Juno so angry that she forbade the nymph ever to say anything again except that last word she was so fond of. But the saddest part of Echo's punishment was that she could not say her own last words. She could only repeat those that other people said.

One day when she was wandering lonely and speechless in the Arcadian forest, Echo saw the handsome youth Narcissus. She fell in love with him at once.

Narcissus was looking for a friend who was lost. He called over and over again, "Where are you?"

Echo longed to tell Narcissus of her love, but all she could do was answer "You?" every time he called. Narcissus grew more and more puzzled by the lovely voice that tossed his last word back to him. He peered through the leafy branches of the forest but he could not see anybody. At last Echo ran from behind the tree where she was hiding and threw her arms around him.

But Narcissus was a strange young man. He did not know how to love, and so he could not understand Echo's love for him. It frightened him. The minute she touched him he ran away as fast as he could.

Echo was so heartbroken and ashamed that she ran away too. She hid in a dark cave, and as time went on she grew thinner and thinner until there was nothing left of her except her voice. But Echo's voice still answers anybody who calls to it.

Narcissus finally did fall in love. Kneeling by the side of a clear pool he saw his own face reflected in the water. He thought it was a water spirit and tried to put his arms around it, but as soon as he touched the water, the image disappeared. Fearful of losing it forever, Narcissus knelt day and night by the pool admiring his own face. He would not leave it even to eat and drink. Like Echo, he grew thinner and thinner. Finally there was nothing left of him but one last breath with which to breathe "Farewell!" to the image in the pool.

Deep in the forest faithful Echo answered, "Farewell."

Where Narcissus had knelt there grew a beautiful white flower. We still call it by his name, "Narcissus."

JASON AND THE GOLDEN FLEECE

King Aeson of Thessaly gave his crown to his brother Pelias. But he told Pelias that he could wear it only until the young prince Jason, Aeson's son, grew to be a man.

But when that time came, Pelias did not want to give up the crown. He told Jason that before he became king he must bring back from Colchis the golden fleece of a sheep that once belonged to King Aeson. The golden fleece hung on a tree which was guarded by a dragon. Pelias knew that many young men had lost their lives in battle with the dragon. Secretly, Pelias hoped that Jason would lose his life too.

Many brave heroes set sail for Colchis with Jason in a great ship which they called the Argo. Among the heroes were Theseus and Hercules. Jason asked Jupiter to protect them all.

The first stopping place of the heroes was an island where an old man lived alone. This old man could see into the future. Jupiter, who liked to keep his plans a secret, had punished the old man in a terrible way. Every time the old man sat down to eat, Jupiter sent the Harpies to snatch his food.

The Harpies were monsters with the heads of women and the wings and bodies and claws of birds. Only the sons of the North Wind could defeat them. Luckily, the sons of the North Wind were on board the Argo. When the Harpies flew down to eat the old man's dinner the sons of the North Wind drew their flashing swords. At that moment Iris, goddess of the rainbow, appeared

and commanded the sons of the North Wind not to kill the Harpies. She also told them that Jupiter had promised that the birds would not snatch the old man's food again.

The old man was so grateful to the heroes that he looked into the future and told them about the dangers ahead. He also told them how to avoid them. One of the dangers was the Clashing Rocks, two great rocks which tossed about in a boiling sea. The old man told the heroes to send a little dove flying ahead of them. When the rocks tossed apart she would fly between them and the heroes could safely follow. This the heroes did. As soon as they had passed safely, the rocks came together. Ever since then the rocks have stayed together, and sailors do not need to be afraid of them any more.

At last the Argonauts, as the heroes were called, came to the land of Colchis. Jason went to the palace to ask the king for the golden fleece.

The king wanted to keep the golden fleece for himself, so he asked Jason to do something he was sure Jason could not do.

"I have two fine bulls," the king said. "Their feet are bronze, and they breathe fire. Yoke them together and plow my field with them. Then sow the teeth of a dragon as though they were seeds. The teeth will grow into an army of soldiers. Cut them down as though they were wheat."

Jason went back to the ship. All night long the Argonauts talked of this impossible thing the king had asked Jason to do. Finally Jason called on the goddess Juno to help him.

Juno decided that the person who could help Jason most was the king's daughter, Medea. Medea had magic powers and she knew magic charms. So Juno asked her son Cupid to pierce Medea's heart with an arrow which would make her fall in love with Jason.

When Medea felt the sting of Cupid's arrow through her heart she hurried to Jason's ship and gave him a magic charm which she told him to rub on his body to protect him from harm. Then she told him that when the army of soldiers rose from the field he must not try to fight them. He must throw a stone among them.

The next morning, after rubbing himself with the magic charm, Jason went to the field where the king had told him to plant the dragon's teeth. The bulls stood waiting, bellowing and breathing fire. Jason reached through the fire, forced the bulls to their knees, and fastened the yoke on them. Then he drove them up and down the field, scattering the dragon's teeth as he went.

When Jason reached the end of the field and saw the army of soldiers that had sprung up behind him he tossed a stone among them. Each soldier thought another had thrown the stone. They started to fight. They fought until they had all killed one another.

Medea knew that the king did not intend to give Jason the golden fleece and that he was already thinking of another impossible task for him. So she offered to help Jason get the golden fleece without the king's knowledge. That night she took him to the secret woods where the dragon guarded the golden fleece. She lulled the dragon to sleep with a magic charm and Jason lifted the

precious fleece from the branch where it hung. Then Jason and Medea hurried to the Argo, and before dawn they were on their way to Greece with the golden fleece.

But there were still dangers ahead for the Argonauts before they reached home. They had to pass by the rock of Scylla, where the waves churned and rolled and threw ships into the whirlpool of Charybdis. The whirlpool could suck a ship down, down to the bottom of the sea. But once more Juno watched over the Argonauts. She guided them safely past the rock and the whirlpool.

Just off the island of Crete, the Argonauts ran short of supplies. They decided to land on the island and look for fresh food and water. But Medea warned them that a monster called Talus lived on Crete and would not allow them to land. Talus was made all of bronze except for one ankle. His ankle was the only place where anybody could hurt him.

When the Argo came a little closer to the island, the Argonauts saw the monster standing high on a cliff. In his hands were tremendous rocks and he shouted that he would throw them at the ship if it came any closer. Then Medea used her magic powers. She made Talus drop one of his rocks, and as the rock fell, it cut the monster's ankle. Slowly the life and strength drained out of Talus, and he fell to the ground.

The Argonauts anchored their ship and went ashore to find fresh food and water for the rest of their journey. After many more days of sailing they reached home with the golden fleece.

PERSEPHONE

Persephone was the daughter of Ceres, goddess of all that grows on earth. Persephone was very beautiful, and Pluto, god of the underworld, fell in love with her. Pluto was used to having his own way, and so he did not bother to ask Persephone if she would like to be his wife. He just stole her and carried her down to the land of darkness in his coal-black chariot.

Persephone's mother Ceres was heartbroken when she found her daughter gone. She searched for her for many months, but she could not find her anywhere. Nobody offered to help her, because everybody was afraid of Pluto's anger.

In her great grief Ceres left Mount Olympus and came to live on earth. She would not allow anything to grow there while Persephone was gone. No seeds sprang up. There was too much sun and too much rain. The winter came and there was no spring to end it.

When Jupiter saw that the earth was dying, he sent his messenger Mercury to the underworld to tell Pluto, Jupiter's brother, that he must send Persephone back to Olympus.

Pluto knew that he could not disobey Jupiter, but he knew that he could trick him. Persephone had eaten nothing since she came to the underworld, for she knew that if she accepted food from the god of darkness she would be tied to him forever. Pluto waited until she was nearly starved, and then he offered her four pomegranate seeds. In her great hunger she ate them. Then Pluto told her she might go back to Olympus with Mercury.

Persephone was welcomed joyfully by her mother and all the gods. Ceres commanded the earth to be green again. The trees were full of fruit and the world was bright. But when Persephone confessed that she had eaten the pomegranate seeds there was sorrow again on Olympus. The trees on earth shed their leaves in sadness. They knew that because Persephone had eaten the pomegranate seeds she would have to return to the underworld for four months every year. For those four months the earth must sleep in darkness and bear no fruit.

That is why, the people of long ago believed, the winter comes and the earth is cold and barren. But at the end of those four cold months, Persephone returns from the dark underworld. She brings with her the green of life and hope.

THESEUS AND THE MINOTAUR

Theseus was the son of Aegus, king of Athens, and Aethra, daughter of the king of Troezen. While Theseus was still a baby, Aegus took him and his mother to Troezen and left them there. Under a big rock he placed his own sword and shield and told Aethra that when Theseus was old enough to move the rock and lift the sword and shield, she must send him to Athens.

When Theseus grew to be a man he rolled away the rock and buckled on his father's sword and shield and set out for Athens. On the way to the city he met many wicked men and beasts, but he overcame them all.

While Theseus and his mother were in Troezen the sorceress Medea had put a spell on King Aegus and married him. Now, when she heard that Theseus had returned, she was afraid that she would have to give up some of her power to him. So she told Aegus that Theseus was not his son and persuaded him to give Theseus a cup of poisoned wine. But just as Theseus was about to drink the wine, Aegus saw the sword and shield and knew that Theseus was really his son.

At that time the whole city of Athens was in mourning. When Theseus asked why this was, his father told him that long ago King Minos of Crete had sent his son to visit Athens. There the young prince had been killed on a wild boar hunt. Once every year since then King Minos had demanded that Aegus send him seven young men and seven maidens to be sacrificed to the Mino-

41

taur, King Minos' favorite monster. The Minotaur lived in the labyrinth that Daedalus had built on Crete long ago. No one had ever been known to escape from the labyrinth's twisting paths and corridors.

When Theseus heard this, he offered to be one of the seven young men who must be sacrificed. On a ship with sails of blackest hue they voyaged to the island where the Minotaur waited. But when Ariadne, King Minos' daughter, saw the strong young warrior, she fell in love with him. She sent for Daedalus and Daedalus gave her the plan of the labyrinth and told her how Theseus could escape.

The next night Ariadne let Theseus out of prison and gave him a sword and a ball of string, as Daedalus had suggested. After telling him how to use these things, Ariadne guided Theseus through the dark streets to the labyrinth. There she unlocked the gate and let Theseus inside and closed the door behind him.

Theseus tied the end of the string to the gate and held the ball in his hand. Unwinding the string behind him he strode through the labyrinth until he saw the Minotaur. The monster roared furiously when it saw the sword. It thought King Minos had tricked it. It tossed its head and charged at Theseus. The labyrinth rang with the sound of battle. But the Minotaur was no match for the strong young warrior. It lay dead at last, and Theseus followed the trail of string out of the labyrinth. Then he and Ariadne let all the other young men and the seven maidens out of prison and sailed home to Greece.

HECTOR AND ACHILLES

In Greece there lived a young man named Achilles who was very brave. Across the blue Aegean Sea, in the city of Troy, there lived another young man named Hector. He too was very brave. He was the son of Priam, the good king of Troy. Achilles and Hector both took pride in protecting other people from danger. They might have been friends, but they were enemies, for they met when their two countries were at war.

The war was called the Trojan War. It started with a silly quarrel when Achilles' father Pelius married the sea nymph Thetis. All the goddesses were invited to the wedding except Eris, the goddess of quarrels. Eris was so angry at being left out that she threw among the guests a golden apple on which she had written "For the fairest." Juno, Venus and Minerva quarreled over the apple all through the wedding. Each one said it was meant for her. Finally they asked Jupiter to decide, but after one look at their angry faces Jupiter thought it best not to take sides with any one of them. He told them to go to Mount Ida in Troy, where King Priam's son Paris was tending his sheep. Paris, he said, could decide the question better than he could.

The goddesses went to Mount Ida and found Paris. Each one begged him to tell her she was the fairest. Juno promised him riches if he would say she was, and Minerva promised him fame. But Venus promised him the most beautiful woman in the world and Paris said Venus was the fairest.

The most beautiful woman in the world was Helen. She was already married to Menelaus, King of Sparta in Greece, but Venus helped Paris to persuade Helen to run away with him to Troy. Immediately Menelaus called on all the young warriors in Greece to buckle on their swords and bring her back.

Among the warriors who sailed for Troy was Achilles. The other warriors believed that not even the great Hector could conquer Achilles because when he was a baby his mother had dipped him in the River Styx. The magic waters of that river were supposed to protect Achilles from all harm.

But Achilles' mother had forgotten one thing. When she held him by his tiny heel to dip him in the river, she forgot that the waters would not touch the bit of skin her hand covered. Anybody could wound Achilles' heel.

The Greeks and Trojans fought the war for Helen for ten long years. The warriors grew tired and quarrelsome. Achilles quarreled with his chief, Agamemnon, and left the battle with all the warriors who were under his command. Agamemnon begged and begged him to come back, but Achilles refused. Finally he did allow his warriors to return. Achilles' dearest friend, Patroclus, took command, and Achilles loaned him his golden armor.

The Trojans had been certain that they would win when they saw Achilles leave the field. Now, when they saw Patroclus in the golden armor they thought Achilles had come back. All but Hector fled inside the city. Hector stood alone, believing that he faced the mightiest of the Greeks. He, too, thought that nobody

could kill Achilles. But he was willing to give his life to protect Troy. Bravely he hurled his spear—and pierced Patroclus to the heart.

When Achilles saw Patroclus fall he rushed from his tent to avenge his friend. Hector stood alone outside the gates of Troy. Achilles charged him with drawn spear. Hector hurled his lance, but it bounced harmlessly off Achilles' shield. Then Achilles threw his spear. The spear struck home and the great Hector fell.

Hector knew that he was so terribly wounded that he could not live. He wanted a hero's funeral. He begged Achilles to give it to him, but Achilles refused. He was still too angry and full of sorrow to be kind. He tied ropes to Hector's feet and fastened the ropes to his chariot and dragged the hero's body back and forth near where Patroclus lay buried. In this way he avenged the death of his friend.

Old Priam, the good king of Troy, was brokenhearted. He opened the gates of the city and came out and begged Achilles for Hector's body. Achilles was so touched by the old man's tears that he gave Priam his son's body. Then he ordered the fighting stopped for twelve days while Hector had a hero's funeral.

During those twelve days Achilles dreamed of peace. He told King Priam he would try to stop the war. He even asked the god Apollo to help him. But Apollo was a friend of Paris. Paris had never forgiven Achilles for killing Hector. He aimed a poisoned arrow at Achilles and Apollo guided the arrow straight to Achilles' heel. Achilles fell and died.

PHAETON

Phaeton's father was the Sun, the great lord of the heavens. Every time Phaeton saw his father's fiery chariot climb the sky his heart beat fast with pride. But when he told the boys at school who his father was they would not believe him. They laughed so hard that Phaeton began to wonder if it was really true. And so he asked his mother for proof.

Phaeton's mother told him to go and ask his father. She packed all Phaeton's belongings neatly in a box and he set forth with them to find the Sun's palace on the edge of the world.

When Phaeton came to the palace he saw his father sitting on his throne wearing his crown of light. The light was so dazzling that Phaeton had to close his eyes. When the Sun saw this he kindly took off his crown and Phaeton opened his eyes.

"Are you really my father?" asked Phaeton.

The Sun said that he was, and he said he could prove it. He would grant Phaeton his dearest wish.

"My dearest wish is to drive your chariot," said Phaeton.

"But I am the only god in heaven who can drive my chariot!" the Sun exclaimed. "You are only half a god. Don't you know that the sky is full of dangers? The Bull, the Lion, the Scorpion —they are all waiting to frighten my horses and wreck my chariot."

But Phaeton insisted, and the Sun could not break his promise. The horses and the golden chariot waited. With a shout of joy, Phaeton mounted the chariot.

Swifter than the wind the horses climbed through the clouds, but the horses knew that it wasn't a god who drove them. They tossed their heads and glared back at the driver with their wild eyes. While Phaeton clung in fright to the rocking chariot they tore this way and that way, almost crashing into the Crab and the Scorpion. With a great burst of speed they rocketed to the very top of the sky, then turned and plunged down, down, down. The earth caught fire. The mountains burned. The rivers turned to steam. The great river Nile fled and hid its head in the desert.

High on Olympus, Jupiter looked down and saw the earth in flames and heard its cries. There was only one thing he could do to save it. He flung a thunderbolt at the chariot.

The chariot exploded, the horses fell into the sea, and Phaeton was swallowed up forever by the mysterious river Eridanus, which no mortal has ever seen.

PERSEUS AND MEDUSA

When Perseus was born his grandfather dreamed that some day the boy would kill him. So he locked the baby and his mother Danaë in a trunk and cast the trunk into the sea. A fisherman on the island of Seriphus found the trunk and brought it to his king, Polydectes. Polydectes gave Perseus and his mother a home in the castle.

But when Perseus grew up, Polydectes was jealous of his strength and courage. He wanted to get rid of the young warrior. So he commanded him to go to Greece and bring back the head of Medusa, who was one of the monsters called Gorgons. He knew very well that whoever looked at Medusa's face would turn to stone.

In Greece Perseus met the god Mercury. Mercury said he would help Perseus to find weapons that would protect him from Medusa. These weapons, Mercury said, belonged to the Nymphs of the North, but only the Gray Women knew where the Nymphs lived. The Gray Women lived where no sun or moon ever shone. But strangest of all, they had only one eye among them. When one finished with the eye, the next one took it and placed it in the middle of her own forehead. When one of the Gray Women removed her eye to pass it on to her sister, Perseus must snatch the eye and hold it until she told him where the Nymphs lived.

Mercury guided Perseus to the twilight land where the Gray Women swam on a great dark pond. They were disguised as swans, their arms were hidden under their long gray wings. Perseus waited until one of them removed the eye from her forehead and then he leaped from his hiding place in the reeds and snatched the eye.

The Gray Women beat the water with their wings and stretched their necks and shrieked with anger. Then Perseus told them who he was and said he would return the eye when they told him where the Nymphs lived. They told him to go to the land of the Hyperboreans who lived at the back of the North Wind. Perseus thanked them and gave them back the eye.

On the way to the land of the Hyperboreans Mercury gave Perseus a beautiful strong sword with which to attack Medusa. The tough scales of the monster would bend an ordinary sword,

he said. Then Minerva came down from Olympus and gave Perseus her polished bronze shield. She told him not to look at Medusa, but to look at the monster's image reflected in the shield. If he did this, he would not turn to stone.

After traveling for many days Perseus and Mercury came to the back of the North Wind where the Nymphs made Perseus welcome. They gave him winged shoes like Mercury's, a magic wallet which would stretch to hold whatever he put into it, and a cap which would make him invisible. Perseus thanked the Nymphs, put on his winged shoes and flew with Mercury to the dark land of the Gorgons. With the sword of Mercury, the shield of Minerva and the gifts of the Nymphs, he was ready to do battle with Medusa.

51

The Gorgons lived on a lonely island in the middle of the sea. Perseus and Mercury crept to the dreadful cave where the monsters lay asleep. Perseus did not look at them. He looked at Minerva's shield instead, and there he saw them reflected. They had the bodies of women but their bodies were covered with golden scales and their hair was hissing snakes.

While Perseus stood gazing at the dreadful scene reflected in his shield, Minerva came to him again and told him which of the monsters was Medusa. This was very important, for the other two monsters were immortal. No one could kill them. Perseus lifted his sword, and while he kept his eyes fixed on the polished shield, Minerva guided his sword. Down came the blade. In one stroke it severed the head of Medusa. Perseus dropped Medusa's head into the magic wallet which stretched to hold and hide it. The other two Gorgons woke up, but Perseus put on the cap that made him invisible and with his winged shoes he flew out of the cave and back to Seriphus.

While Perseus was away Polydectes had ordered a great feast of celebration, for he thought he would never see Perseus again. The feast was still going on when Perseus returned. The brave warrior strode into the palace holding high the shield of Minerva, the magic wallet hanging heavy at his side. The wicked king and his guests turned to look at him in amazement. Before they could look away Perseus plunged his hand into the wallet, drew forth Medusa's head and held it high. The king and all his guests turned to stone.

PEGASUS

In the country of Lycia a terrible monster called the Chimera was frightening everybody. The Chimera had the head of a lion, the body of a goat, and the tail of a serpent.

Iobates, king of Lycia, wanted a hero to kill the Chimera. Just in time a young warrior named Bellerophon came to the court asking if there were some heroic deeds he might do. Iobates asked him to kill the Chimera.

Bellerophon set out willingly on this quest. But first he asked Minerva to help him. Minerva told him that only the winged horse Pegasus could help him fight the Chimera. Then she gave Bellerophon a golden bridle for Pegasus and told him to look for the horse in the meadow early next morning.

At dawn Bellerophon went to the meadow and there was the great white horse nibbling the grass, its wings folded. The horse stood quietly while Bellerophon slipped the golden bridle over its head and mounted. Then it spread its wings and soared. Bellerophon felt like a god.

On the back of the beautiful winged horse Bellerophon set out to find the monster. Pegasus' strong white wings carried them swiftly through the air and it was not long before they saw the Chimera roaming through the dark woods. Bellerophon drew an arrow. Pegasus dropped soft as a bird through the trees and Bellerophon shot the arrow and the arrow found its mark. Enraged, the Chimera snorted fire through its nostrils. Pegasus soared out of reach of the monster and Bellerophon shot another arrow. So the battle went until the Chimera lay dead.

Joyfully Bellerophon flew back to the king who gave him a great feast and many fine presents. Bellerophon became a great favorite of the king, and he and Pegasus fought many more brave battles. Their fame spread throughout the land.

But fame was not good for Bellerophon, who already felt a little like a god. After a while he began to believe he was a god. He even tried to fly on his winged horse to heaven where the heroes dwelt. The gods were patient with him for a long time. Now Jupiter was angry. He sent a gadfly to sting the beautiful Pegasus. The horse threw Bellerophon from its back and soared away, wild and free as before.

For the rest of his life Bellerophon roamed the world alone. Nobody dared to be friendly with the warrior the gods had punished.

CUPID AND PSYCHE

There was a king's daughter named Psyche who was so beautiful that even the goddess Venus was jealous of her. Venus commanded her son Cupid, the god of love and mischief, to shoot into Psyche's heart an arrow that would make her fall in love with someone very ugly. But when Cupid saw Psyche he fell in love with her himself. He never shot the arrow.

Psyche had two sisters and in time they both married. But no young men came begging for Psyche's hand. They were all afraid of her beauty. Psyche's father worried about this. He even asked the oracle of Apollo what to do. And then he must have been sorry that he asked, for the oracle told him to take Psyche to a lonely mountain peak and leave her there until a serpent of the sky came to claim her for his bride.

Alone on the cold mountain peak where her father left her, Psyche waited trembling for the serpent to come lashing down the starry road of heaven to claim her. Then suddenly the warmest, gentlest breeze blew against her cheek. It was the breath of Zephyrus, Cupid's servant. Zephyrus lifted Psyche in his arms and carried her to a golden palace in a green valley.

While Psyche stood wondering and half afraid a voice called her name. She looked around but there was no one there. "Psyche," the voice called, "this is your home."

Psyche went into the golden palace and invisible hands brought her food and drink on a golden tray.

57

"Eat, Psyche," said the same voice she had heard before.

Psyche ate, for she was very hungry. While she was eating, invisible hands played beautiful music on invisible lutes.

That night Psyche's husband came to claim her. She begged for a light so that she could see what he looked like, but he told her to love him and never ask to see his face. He left with the first light of dawn.

At first Psyche enjoyed this strange life, but after a while she grew lonely. She felt odd answering that voice from nowhere, living with people she could not see, bumping into them unawares. So she asked her sisters to visit her.

But when Psyche's sisters saw her happiness they tried to spoil it. They were very jealous.

"How do you know you aren't married to that old serpent after all?" they asked. "You've never seen your husband."

They gave Psyche a lamp to see her husband by and a sword to kill him with if he should prove to be as ugly as they hoped.

That night, as soon as her husband fell asleep, Psyche lighted the lamp and crept to his side. When the light fell on his face she trembled with happiness. There lay Cupid, fairest of all the gods! The longer Psyche gazed at him the more she trembled, and suddenly a drop of oil spilled from the lamp onto Cupid's shoulders. He opened his eyes and looked at her sadly and left the palace without a word.

Psyche was heartbroken. She begged Venus for forgiveness, but Venus was too angry to forgive Psyche immediately. First, Venus

59

said, Psyche must separate a whole roomful of tiny seeds into piles, each of a different kind. And she must do it in just one day or she would never be forgiven.

When Psyche saw the great roomful of seeds she began to cry. Some kindly ants heard her, and seeing how beautiful she was, they took pity on her. Thousands of them came and separated the seeds in no time at all.

But Venus was still angry. She told Psyche that she must also gather the golden fleece from the backs of some vicious sheep. When Psyche saw the sheep she began to cry again, but a voice said, "Wait until the sheep go to sleep. Then you can gather the fleece that has caught on the bushes."

When Psyche brought her the golden fleece Venus was angrier than ever. She sent Psyche to the Underworld to bring back the beauty of Persephone.

Once more the voice helped Psyche. It guided her past the dangers of the Underworld and helped her find the little box where Persephone kept her beauty. The voice warned Psyche not to open the box, and then it guided her back to earth.

Psyche had promised not to open the box, but she did. A mist came out of it that put her fast asleep. She might be sleeping yet if Cupid had not found her and put the mist back into the box. Then Cupid carried Psyche to Jupiter and begged Jupiter to help them escape Venus' jealousy. Jupiter gave Psyche the cup of immortality to drink so that she could live forever, and Cupid and Psyche were happy ever after.

FIRST BOOKS
classified by subject
Some titles are listed in more than one category

...e ARTS

...itecture
...et
...s
...r
...ving

Gardening
How to Fix It
Jazz
Music
Paintings
Photography

Poetry
Puppets
Rhythms
Stage Costume and
  Make-Up

...MMUNICATIONS

...ries
...es and Ciphers
...guage & How To
...se It

Letter Writing
Maps and Globes
Measurement
Printing

Public Libraries
Teaching Machines
Television
Words

...IENCE

...lanes
...rctic
...haeology
...hitecture
...onomy
...omobiles
...s
...s
...ges
...es
...r
...servation
...on
...h

Electricity
Food
Glaciers
Glass
Human Senses
Light
Machines
Mammals
Maps and Globes
Measurement
Microbes
Mining
Ocean
Photography
Plants
Prehistoric Animals
Rhythms

Roads
Science Experiments
Sea Shells
Snakes
Sound
Space Travel
Stone Age Man
Stones
Submarines
Television
Tools
Trains
Trees
Tropical Mammals
Water
Weather
Wild Flowers

...ORTS & HOBBIES

...eball
...ketball
...s' Cooking
...toons for Kids
...ss
...stmas Joy
...es and Ciphers

Dogs
Dolls
Football
Gardening
Horses
How to Fix It
Jokes
Magic

Photography
Physical Fitness
Sailing
Stones
Surprising Facts
Swimming

SOCIAL STUDIES
United States

Atlas
American History
American Revolution
California Gold Rush
The China Clippers
Civil War Land Battles
Civil War Naval Actions
Congress
Constitution
Early Settlers

Hawaii
Holidays
Indian Wars
Indians
National Monuments
National Parks
Negroes
New England
New World Explorers

Oregon Trail
Panama Canal
Pioneers
Presidents
Supreme Court
United Nations
War of 1812
Washington, D.C.
World War I
World War II

The World About Us

Africa
Ancient Bible Lands
Ancient Egypt
Ancient Mesopotamia
  and Persia
Ancient Greece
Ancient Rome
Antarctic
Archaeology
Australia
Barbarian Invaders
Brazil
Canada

Communist China
Congo
England
Eskimos
Festivals
France
Ghana
India
Israel
Italy
Japan
Kings
Medieval Man
Mediterranean

Mexico
Netherlands
New Zealand
Ocean
Pakistan
South America
Soviet Union
United Nations
Vikings
West Germany
West Indies
World War I
World War II

People and Products

Conservation
Cotton
Cowboys

Firemen
Food
Glass

Nurses
Supermarkets
Water

LITERATURE & LANGUAGE ARTS

Codes and Ciphers
Color
Fairy Tales
Language & How To
  Use It

Letter Writing
Legendary Beings
Maps and Globes
Mythology
Mythical Beasts

Norse Legends
Poetry
Printing
Teaching Machines
Words

TRANSPORTATION

Airplanes
Automobiles
Boats
Bridges

Maps and Globes
Panama Canal
Roads
Ships

Space Travel
Trains
Water

61

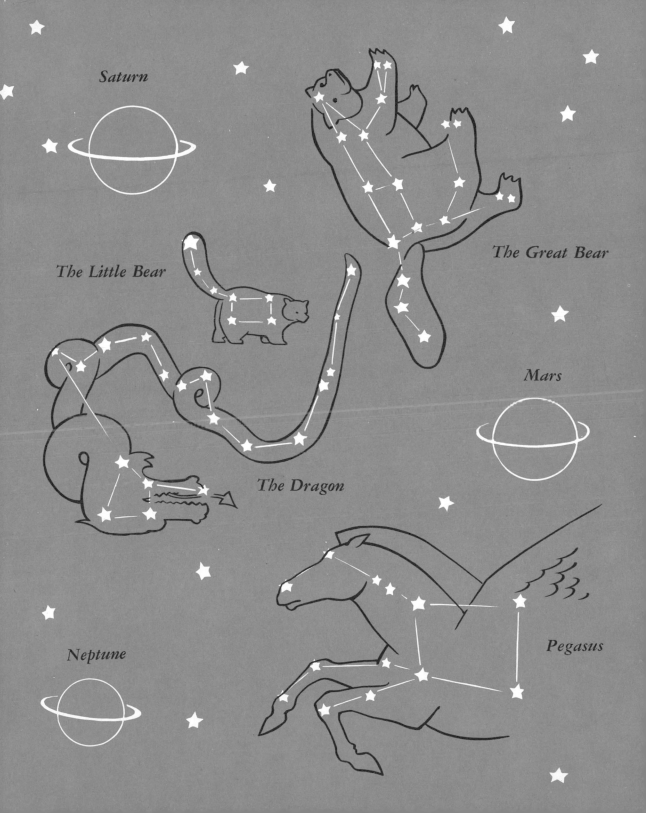

Saturn

The Great Bear

The Little Bear

Mars

The Dragon

Neptune

Pegasus